SCHOLASTIC INC.

FOR ALEX COX!

KEEP SPREADING THE AWESOMENESS!

ISBN 978-1-338-31454-0

18 17 16 15 14 22 23 24

Printed in the U.S.A. 40

First Scholastic printing, January 2019

Edited by Tara Walker and Jessica Burgess
Designed by Ben Clanton and Andrew Roberts

The artwork in this book was rendered in colored pencil, watercolor and ink, and colored digitally.
The text was handlettered by Ben Clanton.

Photos: (waffle) © Tiger Images/Shutterstock; (strawberry) © Valentina Razumova/Shutterstock; (pickle) © dominitsky/Shutterstock; (boom box) © valio84sl/Thinkstock; (jars) © choness/Thinkstock; (peanuts) © Zoonar/homydesign/Thinkstock; (jam on bread) © George Doyle/Thinkstock; (peanut butter toast) © NicholasBPhotography/Thinkstock

CONTENTS

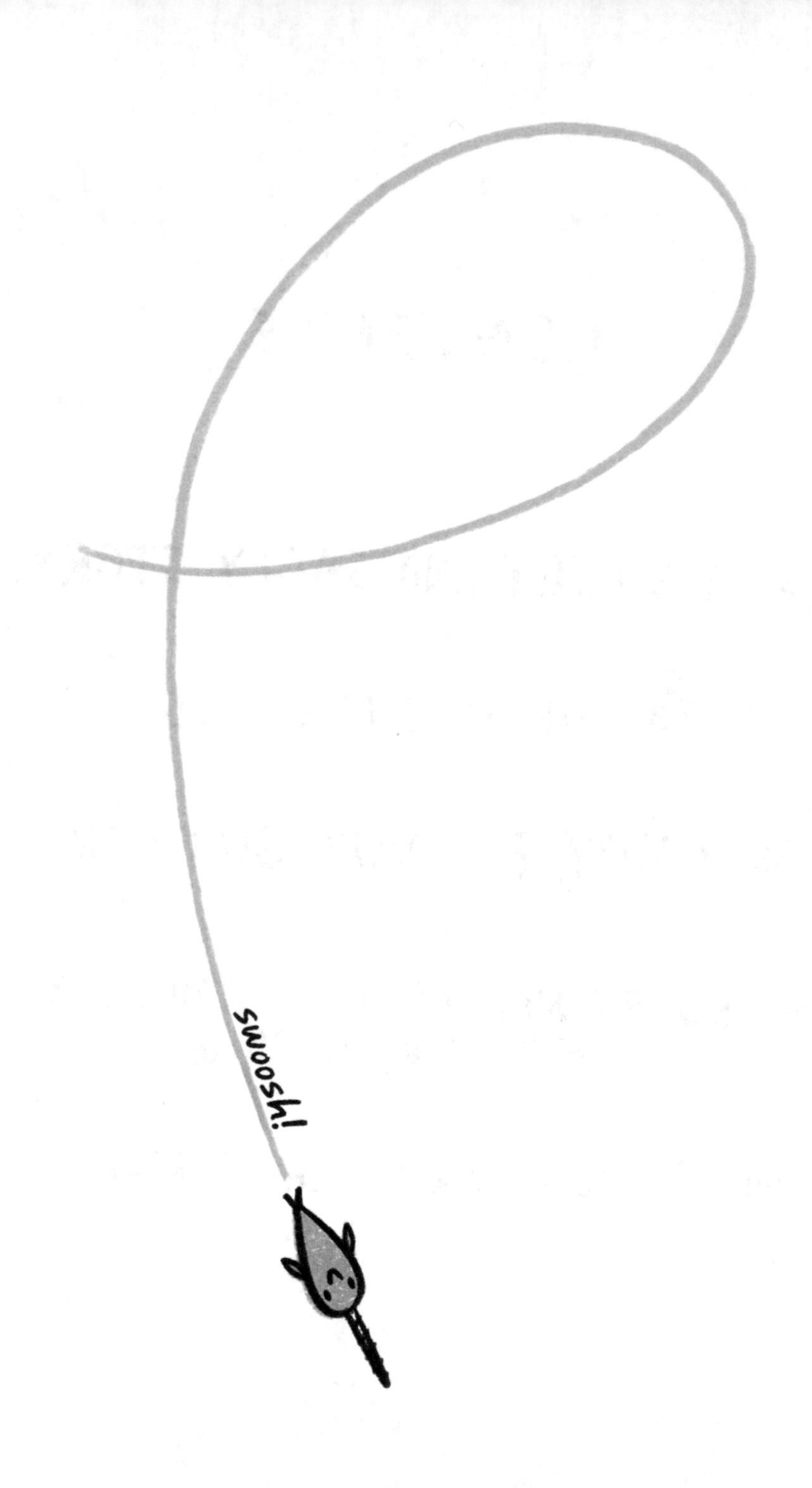
swoosh!

A SWEET AND SALTY STORY!

AHOY, JELLY!
WHAT IS THAT SMALL, STRANGE WAFFLE YOU'RE EATING?

nom
nom
nom

UM... NARWHAL,
THIS IS **NOT** A WAFFLE.
IT IS A PEANUT BUTTER COOKIE.

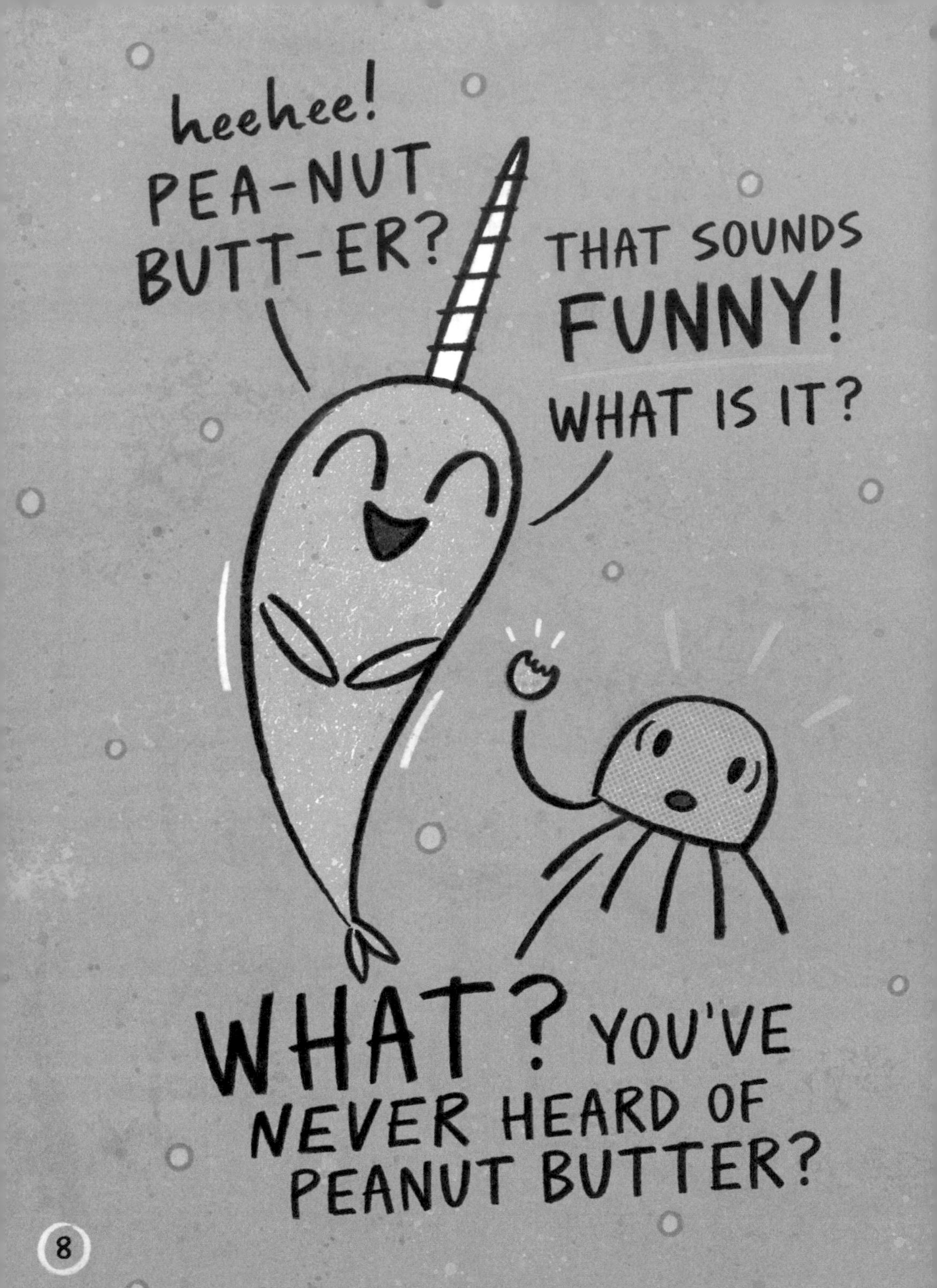

heehee!
PEA-NUT
BUTT-ER?

THAT SOUNDS
FUNNY!
WHAT IS IT?

WHAT? YOU'VE
NEVER HEARD OF
PEANUT BUTTER?

DOES IT TASTE LIKE A WAFFLE?

UM... NO.

LIKE STRAWBERRIES? PICKLES? STIR-FRIED LICORICE?
NO, NO AND ICK!

MAYBE IT TASTES LIKE STIR-FRIED PICKLE LICORICE ON STRAWBERRY WAFFLES!

YUCK!
HAVE YOU ACTUALLY EATEN SOMETHING LIKE THAT BEFORE?

NO, NOT REALLY!
ACTUALLY, I PRETTY MUCH
ONLY EAT
WAFFLES!

PHEW!

WAIT A MINUTE...
ONLY WAFFLES?

THAT CAN'T BE TRUE.
WHAT ABOUT....SPAGHETTI?
YOU MUST HAVE HAD
SPAGHETTI BEFORE.

SPA-WHAT-AY?

SERIOUSLY? WHAT ABOUT... ICE CREAM?

NOPE!

THAT IS JUST WRONG. PIZZA?

UM... NO.

MASHED POTATOES?

IS THAT ANYTHING LIKE MASHED WAFFLES?
MASHED WAFFLES? UM...REALLY?
YOU MUST HAVE HAD SOMETHING OTHER THAN WAFFLES!

CAKE? APPLES?
CHEESE? PIE?
ARTICHOKES?
MARSHMALLOWS?
GUACAMOLE?
UH...SUSHI?
FRENCH FRIES?

NOPE!
NOPE!
NOPITY...
NOPE!

NARWHAL, YOU CAN'T JUST EAT ONLY WAFFLES!
HERE! TRY THIS PEANUT BUTTER COOKIE.

WHY?

HAVE YOU EVER HEARD OF "TOO MUCH OF A GOOD THING"?

THAT'S SILLY! HOW CAN YOU HAVE TOO MANY WAFFLES?

RIGHT... NEVER MIND.

BUT MAYBE YOU'LL LIKE THIS COOKIE EVEN MORE THAN WAFFLES!

heehee!
GOOD ONE, JELLY! NOTHING IS BETTER THAN A WAFFLE!
HOW DO YOU KNOW UNLESS YOU TRY IT?

THANKS, JELLY, BUT I THINK I'LL STICK WITH WAFFLES!

JUST ONE LITTLE BITE?

I TELL YOU WHAT,
I'LL MAKE YOU AN
EXTRA LARGE
WAFFLE IF YOU JUST
TRY THIS PEANUT
BUTTER COOKIE.

HOW BIG WOULD THIS EXTRA LARGE WAFFLE BE?
EVEN BIGGER THAN YOU!

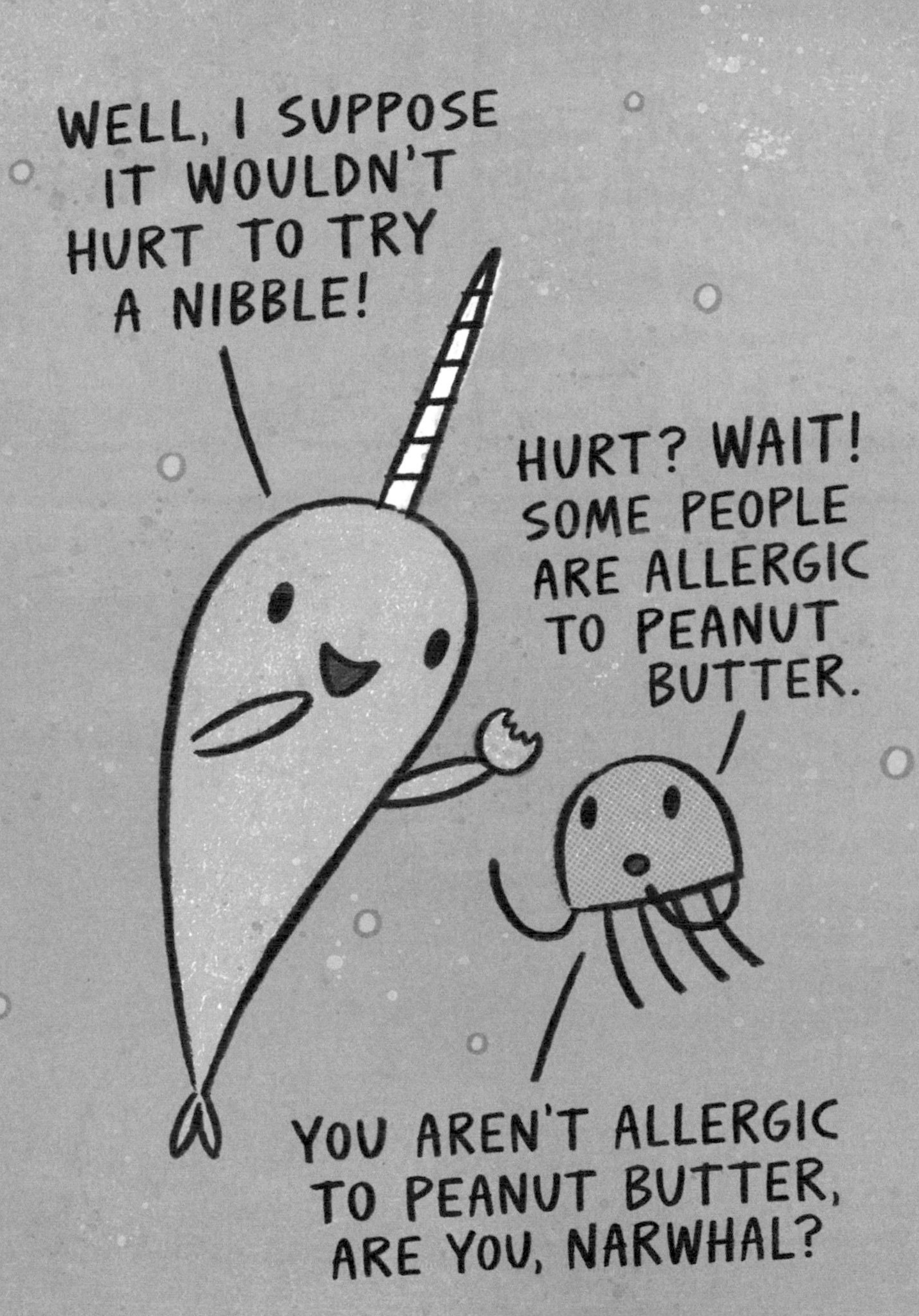
WELL, I SUPPOSE IT WOULDN'T HURT TO TRY A NIBBLE!
HURT? WAIT! SOME PEOPLE ARE ALLERGIC TO PEANUT BUTTER.
YOU AREN'T ALLERGIC TO PEANUT BUTTER, ARE YOU, NARWHAL?

* THE ALLERGIC AQUATIC ANIMALS AWARENESS ASSOCIATION ADVISES CAUTION WHEN TRYING A COMMON ALLERGEN.

OKAY, HERE I GO!
ONE TEENY TINY
TASTE!

nibble
nibble

SO WHAT DO
YOU THINK?

IT'S FIN TASTIC!

SO SWEET!
nom nom

nom
SO SALTY!

IT'S YUMMY!
nom nom
nom

SMACK! SMACK!
IT'S SCRUMP-TIOUS!
nom nom

IT'S YUMPTIOUS!
IT'S...
IT'S...

ALL GONE!
WHOOPS!

DELICIOUS FACTS

SCIENTISTS BELIEVE NARWHALS SUCK UP THEIR FOOD WHOLE AND EAT MAINLY FISH.

MOST JELLYFISH STING THEIR PREY WITH THEIR TENTACLES BEFORE EATING IT.

BLUE WHALES (THE LARGEST ANIMAL EVER) EAT MAINLY TINY LITTLE KRILL. THEY EAT OODLES OF THEM. AS MANY AS 40 MILLION KRILL PER DAY!

HUMPBACK WHALES WORK TOGETHER TO CREATE COMPLEX BUBBLE NETS TO CORRAL FISH TO EAT.

SEA CUCUMBERS EAT ALL SORTS OF THINGS, INCLUDING POOP.

TIGER SHARKS ARE OFTEN REFERRED TO AS "THE TRASH CANS OF THE SEA" BECAUSE THEY WILL EAT JUST ABOUT ANYTHING, FROM PIGS TO TIRES TO EXPLOSIVES.

AHOY, PEANUT BUTTER?

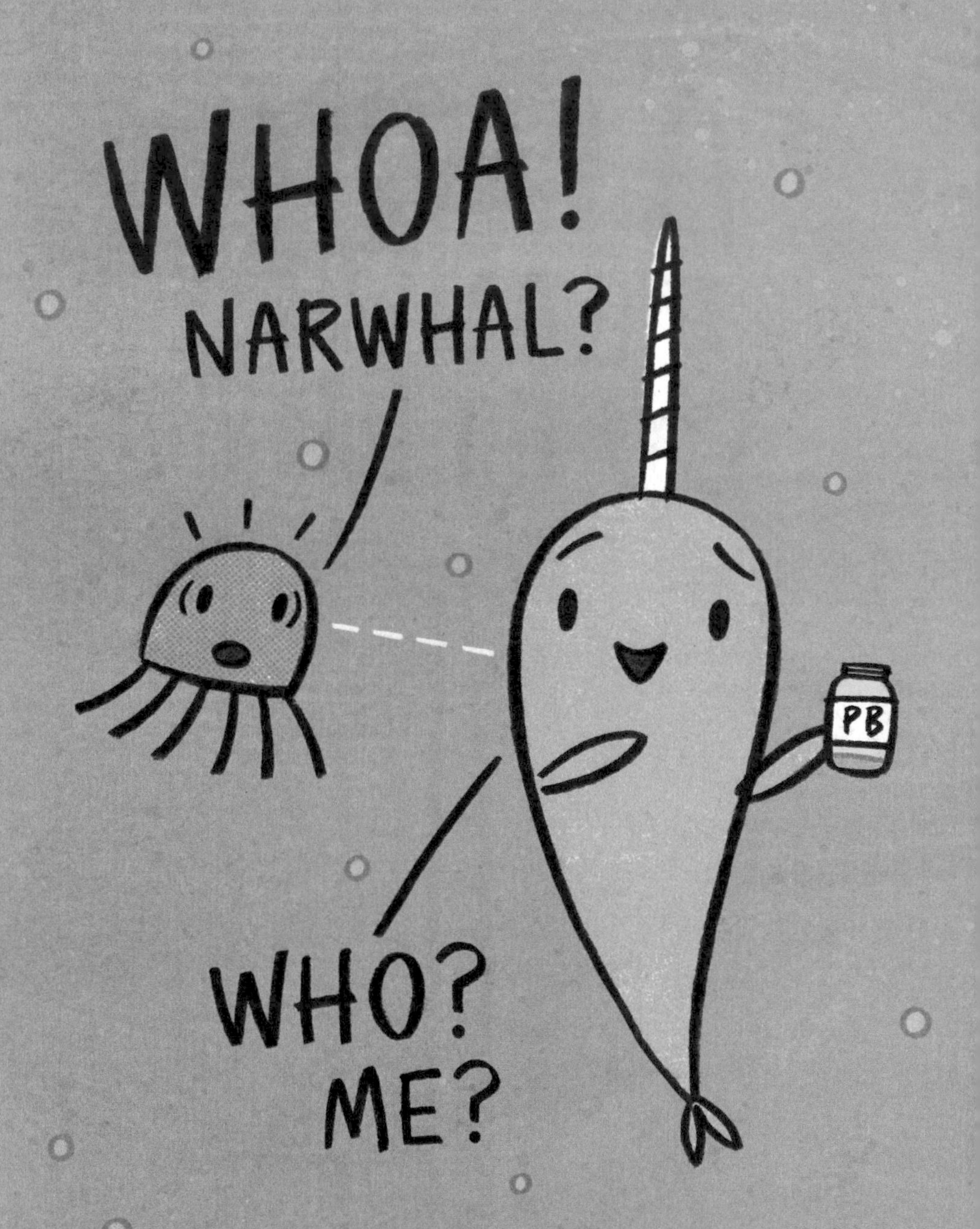
WHOA!
NARWHAL?
PB
WHO?
ME?

YES, YOU! NARWHAL, WHAT HAPPENED? YOU'RE ALL—

OH, MY NAME ISN'T NARWHAL. MY NAME IS PEANUT BUTTER.

PEANUT BUTTER? THAT IS NOT A NAME!

IT IS NOW! I USED TO GO BY NARWHAL, BUT...
PB

...I LOVE PEANUT BUTTER SO MUCH I DECIDED TO CHANGE MY NAME. SEE!
PB
AHOY! MY NAME IS
PEANUT BUTTER

WHAT? YOU CAN'T JUST CHANGE YOUR NAME!

WHY NOT?

BECAUSE! IT ISN'T NORMAL!

OH.

WELL, I'VE NEVER REALLY WANTED TO BE NORMAL. BESIDES, THIS ISN'T THE FIRST TIME I'VE CHANGED MY NAME.
PB

IT ISN'T?

NOPE,
I USED
TO BE
CALLED
FRED.

FRED? YOUR REAL
NAME IS FRED?

WELL,
BEFORE
FRED
I WAS
BOB.

BOB?
SERIOUSLY?

YEP!

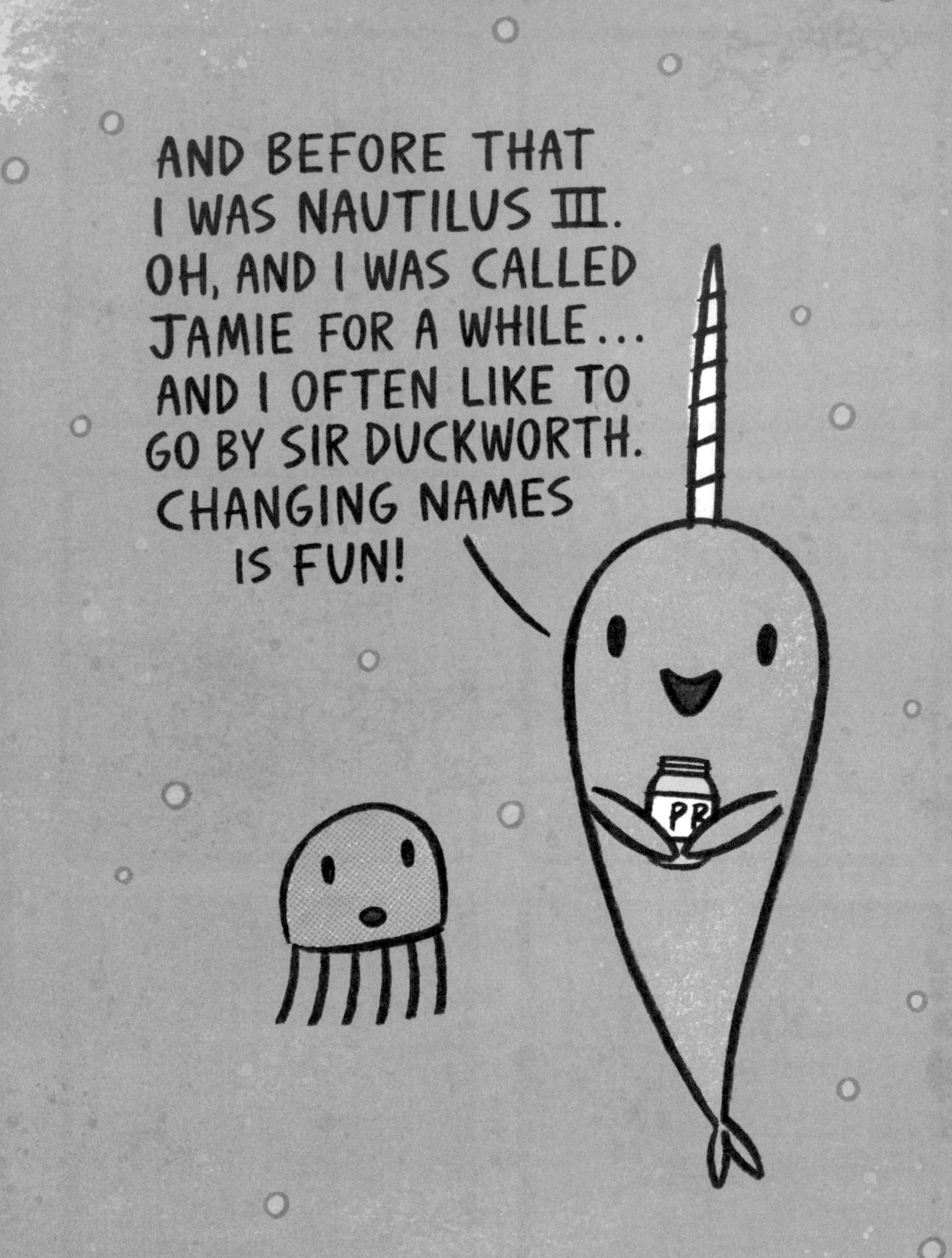

AND BEFORE THAT
I WAS NAUTILUS III.
OH, AND I WAS CALLED
JAMIE FOR A WHILE...
AND I OFTEN LIKE TO
GO BY SIR DUCKWORTH.
CHANGING NAMES
IS FUN!

BUT WHAT IS YOUR REAL NAME?

MY REAL NAME?

YES! THE NAME YOUR PARENTS GAVE YOU!

NAR WHAL!

SO . . . YOU ARE NARWHAL?

I'M PEANUT BUTTER!

UGH! LOOK, PEANUT BUTTER OR NARWHAL OR FRED OR WHATEVER YOU ARE CALLING YOURSELF... DON'T YOU THINK YOU'RE TAKING THIS PEANUT BUTTER THING A BIT TOO FAR?

I MEAN... HOW MUCH PEANUT BUTTER HAVE YOU EATEN?
I'M NOT EXACTLY SURE... I'VE BEEN EATING IT NONSTOP EVER SINCE THAT COOKIE...

HMMM... LOOKS LIKE I'VE FINISHED ANOTHER JAR.
PB

TIME TO GO START
A NEW ONE!
PB

SEE YA, FLOYD!
PB

FLOYD?

FLOYD...

SUPER WAFFLE AND STRAWBERRY SIDEKICK VS. PB&J

by ~~Narwhal~~ Peanut Butter and ~~Jelly~~ Floyd

BUT BEFORE THEY CAN TAKE A SLICE OUT OF THAT PICKLE...
PB&J TIME!

SANDWICH!

YOU'RE STUCK, PICKLE!

I THOUGHT WE WERE THE GREATEST DUO!
THAT PICKLE WAS NO BIG DILL!

BUT WHAT'S THIS? JEALOUS GELATINOUS JAM!
J!
I'M IN A JAM!

SUPER WAFFLE AND STRAWBERRY SIDEKICK TO THE RESCUE!

THAT JAM IS NO MATCH FOR THIS JAM!
CLICK!

BOOM BOOM BOOM
PHEW!

PB & J-WAFFLE-'BERRY TIME!

PEANUT

A.K.A. mini
NARWHAL

NARWHAL?!
OR...ER...
PEANUT BUTTER?
AHOY, FLOYD!
A.K.A. JELLY!

WHAT'S HAPPENED TO YOU NOW?
WHAT DO YOU MEAN?

WHAT DO I MEAN? YOU'RE TINY!
OH, THAT!

WELL, WHEN I WOKE UP THIS MORNING I WAS THE SIZE OF A PEANUT. I THINK IT MIGHT HAVE SOMETHING TO DO WITH ALL THE PEANUT BUTTER I'VE BEEN EATING.

YOU REALLY NEED TO GIVE THIS PEANUT BUTTER THING A BREAK.
OH, WELL, ABOUT THAT...

...I GUESS I'LL HAVE TO. I'VE EATEN ALL THE PEANUT BUTTER IN THE WHOLE WORLD WIDE WATERS!

ALL OF IT?!
YEP!

BURP!

WHOA! OKAY...
BUT WHAT ARE WE GOING TO DO ABOUT YOUR BEING MINI?
DO?

YES! AREN'T YOU WORRIED YOU'LL BE PEANUT-SIZED FOREVER?
NOT REALLY!

BUT HOW WILL YOU PLAY ULTIMATE CANNONBALL WITH ME?

AND YOUR TUTU WON'T FIT!

YOUR CAPE WON'T EITHER!

SHARK MIGHT EAT YOU BY ACCIDENT!
OR
YOU MIGHT SHRINK INTO NOTHING!
GULP!
Ahoy!
POOF!

YOU COULD GET STUCK IN A BUBBLE!
wheeee!
OR
A WAVE COULD WASH YOU TO ANTARCTICA!
IF ELEPHANTS LIVED IN THE WATER, ONE COULD STEP ON YOU! OR SUCK YOU UP ITS TRUNK!
SNORT
CHILLAX, FLOYD!

HOW CAN I CHILLAX?!
THIS IS AWFUL!
HOW ARE YOU OKAY WITH THIS?

BECAUSE OF
THE WAFFLES!

NOW THAT I AM SUPER SMALL
ALL THE WAFFLES WILL
SEEM HUGE TO ME!

I CAN EAT
GIANT
WAFFLES!

OH.

GOOD POINT!

THE NEXT DAY...

AHOY, JELLY!
A.K.A. FLOYD!
ACK! WHAT? HOW? YOU'RE ENORMOUS!
YEP! PRETTY MUCH! MUST HAVE BEEN ALL THOSE GIANT WAFFLES!

ISN'T IT
SUPER?!

BUT I THOUGHT YOU LIKED BEING TINY.

I DID! BUT...

. . . NOW THAT I'M ENORMOUS

I CAN EAT OODLES OF WAFFLES! I'LL BREAK THE WORLD RECORD FOR WAFFLE EATING!

THAT IS . . . INGENIOUS!

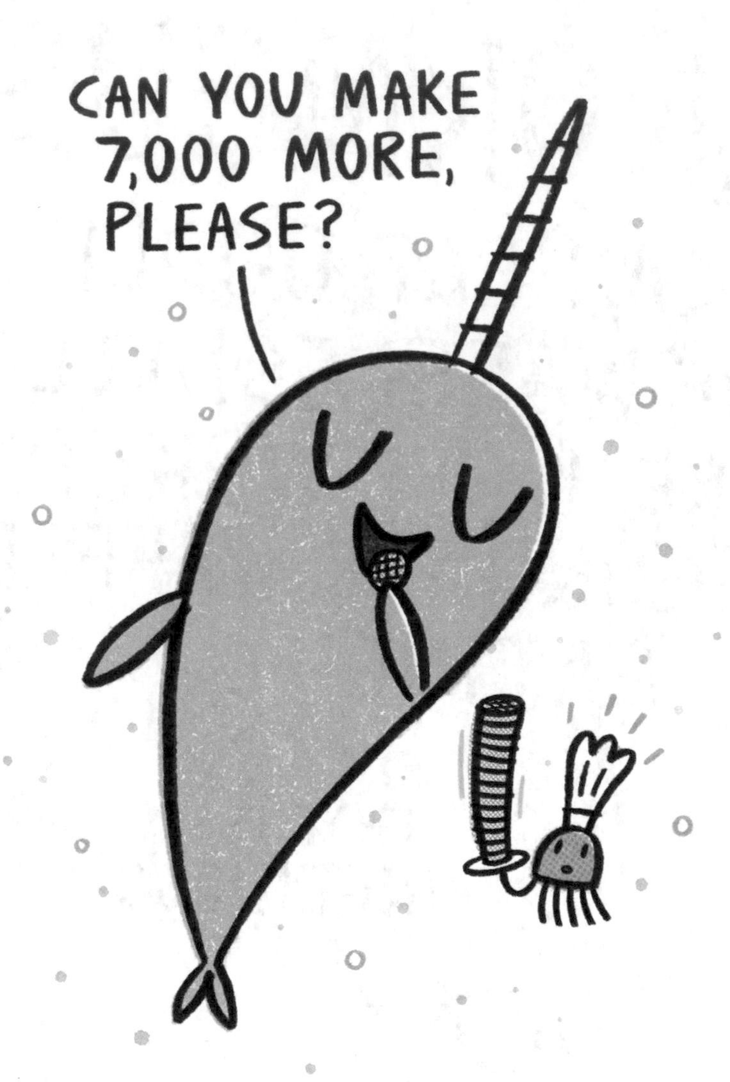
CAN YOU MAKE
7,000 MORE,
PLEASE?